Esquire cartoon album

25th ANNIVERSARY VOLUME

Esquire cartoon album

PUBLISHED BY ESQUIRE, INC.

NEW YORK, NEW YORK, 1957

DISTRIBUTED BY DOUBLEDAY & COMPANY, INC.

GARDEN CITY, NEW YORK, 1957

25th ANNIVERSARY VOLUME

ESQUIRE CARTOON ALBUM

Printed in the United States of America

A book of cartoons needs an introduction no more than the human body needs an appendix. But books of cartoons go on getting provided with introductions, apparently for no better reason than we go on being provided with appendices — we and they both seem to come that way.

Especially in the case of an Esquire book of cartoons would an introduction appear to be unnecessary. The best proof we can cite in support of that contention is the fact that, ever since 1940, every time we've got out any collection of Esquire material in book form, we seem to have devoted a measurable portion of our introduction space to explaining that each such volume *wasn't* a book of Esquire cartoons.

In introducing that perennial best seller *The Bedside Esquire,* we sidled up to the subject by taking a side swipe at the cartoons, saying "Any oaf can enjoy a picture. Esquire's have been cut out and hung up (guess that was before the word 'pin-up' had been coined) in Congo huts as well as American college dormitories. But it takes a mind to make the most of words. That's why it's only natural that Esquire has been much more widely looked at than read."

Elsewhere in that same introduction we said, "Sunny side up, Esquire is just a picture book, wherein the Petty girl's is the face that has launched a thousand quips. There's your darling of the dormitories and belle of the barber shops. How that one gets around!" We went on to say that *The Bedside Esquire* was fashioned out of Esquire's other side, the side that had been so heavily overshadowed by the pictures: "Sometimes this editor, weary of hearing the cartoons talked about as if they characterized the contents as a whole, has been tempted to term it The Esquire Nobody Knows."

Two things about the cartoons in Esquire used to burn us up. One was the endless succession of radio comedians' jokes, building up from a thousand and one angles to a final punch line to the general effect of "Oh, you mean they have *words* in that magazine, too!" The other was the plaint we used to hear, from about the end of 1934 onward, that "the cartoons aren't as funny as they used to be."

This book has a bearing on both those points. First, it represents as nearly as possible Esquire without words, being crammed with pictures from end to end, using words only to the irreducible minimum degree that they are needed to pin the point on the pictures, and second a heavy proportion of its pictures are from Esquire's vintage years '33 through say '37.

Now whether the cartoons really were funnier in those early years than they are nowadays is something that each person can only decide for himself.

Our own ill-tempered inclination, every time we were told that the cartoons weren't as funny as they used to be, was to say "Brother, neither are you, neither is anybody and neither is anything."

We think, for instance, that one cartoon in the September '57 issue is as funny as any we've ever published. It shows a man about to be executed, given a last cigarette by the officer in command of the firing squad, and commenting, "Say, these really *are* milder."

Now, conceivably, in an age or in a country without cigarette advertising of any kind, that cartoon could be utterly pointless. But, today, with television adding the earnest efforts of high-priced talent to try to convince you at every possible opportunity that this or that cigarette really *is* milder, it seems even more pointed than it might have if it had appeared in our pages anytime before 1948 or '49.

By the same token, many of the cartoons of the past, dealing with NRA or WPA, and boondoggling and leaf-raking and That Man in the White House, must seem comparatively pointless. If you remember them as being funnier than the comparable cartoons of today it probably means either that you reacted more strongly then to the events or situations from which they reflected their humor, or that those events or situations were richer in humorous possibilities than comparable ones today.

Another factor, of course, is that Esquire's cartoons, in its earliest days, were much more of a novelty, in relation to other cartoons, than they can ever hope to be again. For one thing, there was the element of color.

When Esquire was new, no American magazine had ever devoted full-color pages to cartoons, although a few European magazines, such as *La Vie Parisienne* and the Munich *Simplicissimus* had been doing so for years. But in the intervening near-quarter century, the parade has caught up with the leader, as it were, as cartoons in full-color have long since become a commonplace routine of a raft of other American magazines.

Another factor, equally true if in lesser degree, is in the content of the cartoons themselves. As we said four years back in *The Esquire Treasury,* we long ago conceded to *The New Yorker* a near-monopoly on sophisticated whimsy, so we set out in our early days to get a corner on something known (if only to ourselves) as Whamsy. Based on the principle of aesthetics designated in the textbooks as *Einfühlung,* it represented as close an approach to audience-participation as the cartoon could ever come, short of some printing-press equivalent of 3D or Vista-Vision. The most memorable example of this "Wanna Make Something Out of It?" school of comic art was undoubtedly the drawing of the Petty girl looking you straight in the eye (after the manner of Uncle Sam in the recruiting posters, so that from whatever angle you regard it there's no escaping that direct gaze) and captioned, simply but eloquently, "Oh, you would, would you?"

Cartoons like that brought scads of letters asking us to explain the point. We had to answer that there wasn't any, except as made by the mind of the beholder.

Now this kind of cartoon, the pictorial twin of the Shaggy Dog Story in verbal humor, utterly pointless unless you are able and inclined to make it very pointed yourself, is present in considerable quantity in this book, culled as it is in so great measure from the magazine's early years. It is also, admittedly, very scarce in Esquire's pages in these latter years.

Again, it's a question of comparative novelty. We were first with this type of pictorial humor. But we always considered it, like paprika, something to be used sparingly and with discretion. In the course of the years, other magazines have sprung up, based almost entirely on a distorted over-emphasis of this one aspect of Esquire's original formula, and they in turn have bred imitators of their imitatings, to a degree where vulgarity and coarse bad taste have passed the point of no return.

Here it is not a question of the race having caught up with the leader, but rather of the pack having taken off at such a wild tangent, off course and across boundaries where, like another leader who knew the virtue of moderation in all things, we simply "do not choose to run."

That, however, is a point of future magazine policy that need not concern us here, except as it may affect your status as either a present or potential subscriber to Esquire, since this is a retrospective collection. Maybe it's even a sales argument for this book: "Get 'em here, since you won't see their like in Esquire again."

But actually, as you will see as you go through the book, there is only a paprika-like sprinkling of the old-time Whamsy, even here, where the best of four and twenty years of Esquire's cartoons have been assembled.

Our one test, in selecting some five hundred-odd cartoons from among the ten thousand-odd that have appeared in the magazine to date, was simply, "Is it still funny today?" We'll feel satisfied if you are inclined to agree, in something over three out of ten cases, that it is. After all, .333 is still a winning batting average in any league.

We are surprised to find how little the great majority of the drawings in this volume had dated, though they span almost a quarter-century. Maybe this supports our original contention, when the magazine was new, that we hoped to make a majority of our cartoons equally classifiable under the headings of both Art and Humor.

The contributor with the greatest number of cartoons in this book is E. Simms Campbell, with Howard Baer as the runner-up. Campbell is now unique in that, of the hundreds who have appeared in our pages since the first issue in the fall of '33, he is the only contributor, of either text or graphic features, never to have missed a single issue.

More or less complete details about the other contributors will be found in the only other place in this volume where words are bunched together more than a sentence at a time.

So without bunching any more together, here it is. The best of Esquire, twenty-four years worth, sunny side up.

ARNOLD GINGRICH

Publisher of Esquire

"*Good heavens! Clothes certainly do make the man!*"

"Louie, you're a goddam jewel!"

"Practice real loud, dear—Mama is going to collect Daddy's insurance"

"How d'ya spell polygamy?"

"Black? Why do you always have to be conspicuous?"

"That skylight pays my rent!"

*"The efficiency expert advised me to marry her
and hire a good secretary"*

"A woman in my room?—Sir—you underestimate me!"

*"—when last seen was wearing a dress suit
and running like hell!"*

"It's a pretty big crew to put to work on a dog house, but you know the union"

"I had a big day today, dear—I missed out on two ten thousand a year jobs and an eight thousand dollar executive position with a share in the profits"

"*Just think that two hours ago I was only a wrong number!*"

"John, dear, don't you think you should pay
more attention to Cousin Elizabeth?"

"Don't hold it s-ho damned high"

"Call me at nine!"

"My other boss always gave me a raise when he got fresh—
you just get fresh"

"Reminds me of a woman's curves. Everything
reminds me of a woman's curves"

"You don't think mama was a naughty girl tonight, do you?"

"Put it on his nose—but don't hurt him!"

"Ef yew be one o' Lem Hopkins' kids, git on home—
ef yor one o' mine git on into th' house"

"Papa!"

"Calling all police cars—wake up—it is morning—wake up!"

*"If it's a hat, madam, you can exchange it
on the fourteenth floor"*

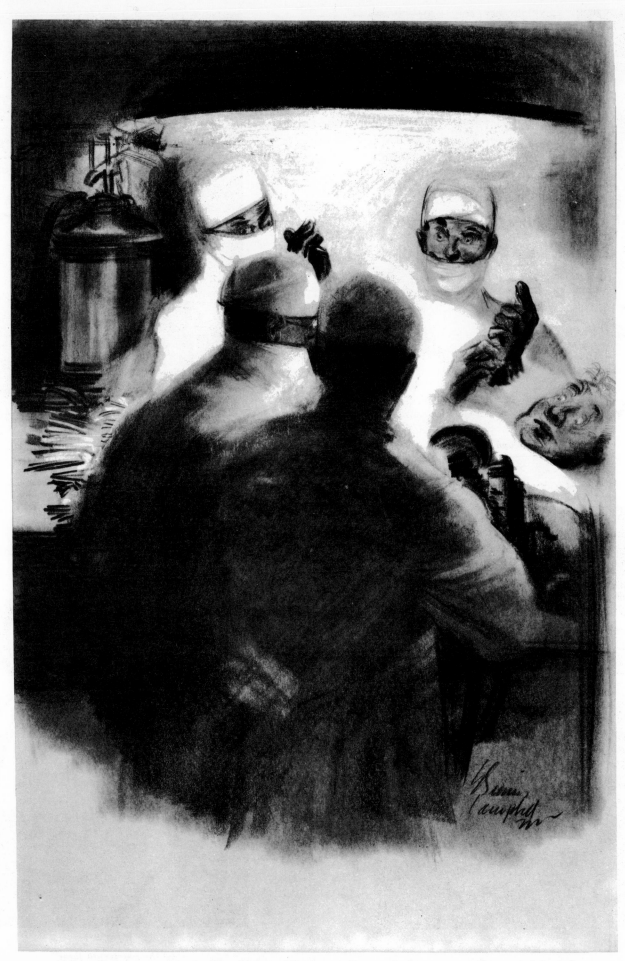

"Gentlemen—this is Mr. Dean Clark, author of the currently sensational novel, 'All Doctors Are Quacks'"

"Gad, Milton, can't you sing anything besides 'Seated One Day at the Organ'?"

"Hey! You wit' th' blue shirt—duck!"

"And if we catch one . . . then can we go home?"

"Phooey!"

"Of course I can live on $1000 a month — but what will you live on?"

"Pardon me, is this seat taken?"

"Shod?—I thought you said shot!"

"Well, well, my old school teacher—H'ya, skunk!"

"—and then, while your heart is pounding in your throat, she drops the last rose and stands naked on the stage"

"Well, I don't know—I was really looking for something cute to make a lamp out of"

"The stork brought you—now shut up!"

*"How long ago was it, Mr. McKenna, that you started imagining
that people were staring at you?"*

"Duchess, you don't mean to sit there and tell me—"

"He's the gentleman who came up to complain about the noise!"

"...and this one has _everything_"

"Take a postcard to my wife, Miss Smith"

"Well, couldn't you just sign an X then?
You know—two crossed lines"

"It's no use—I'll have to get another stenographer"

"Somebody's throwing rice pudding, dear"

"There's a mink, from a rat, on a cat!"

"One each, please . . . driver's, dog, marriage and hunting"

"When I'm reasoning with you, you shut up!"

"The liquor has run out, sir!"

"This guy gets lost every week end"

"Spivvins pushed his 2,000,000th doorbell today!"

"Pardon me, but is this the YMCA?"

"Go ahead—sit on it awhile and see what happens!"

"We'll change at Louisville and again at Miami!"

"Swee-e-t Ad-o-line—!"

"All right, go home to your mother! A lot of sympathy
you'll get from an incubator"

*"You know that beauty contest they're having in the Ritz ballroom Saturday afternoon?
I won it tonight"*

"There's an author dropped in with a manuscript, Fingers—
what'll I do, give him a rejection slip?"

"Oh! Pardon me, Sergeant!"

"I pass"

"That's what I like about a big city—everybody minds their own business!"

"All that happened in a rumble seat?"

"Sure, we'd love to come, Wetzel. But don't you go telling me it's informal and then show up wearing a shirt"

"Everyone else gets three strikes—how come your son gets six?"

"That's all right, I don't mind waiting"

"What's he talking about—a fish, a horse race, or a putt?"

"Congratulations! It's a great story! Now all we have to do
is change the plot, develop new characters
and think up a better title"

"Of course I appreciate your acting as best man, Bob—
but it's all over now and you're supposed to go home"

"Okey doke, lady, the sink's fixed!"

"Shall I take the pin out, sir?"

"My husband and I enjoy your parties so much, Mr. Green"

"Tell them to go to hell—in a nice way of course"

*"We're inaugurating a floor-show tonight, so
we'll have to eliminate this center table"*

"*Let's postpone it — this is a hell of a day to get married!*"

"And then you could use this space for a playroom"

"By the way, just what was it you said that I didn't like?"

"Oh, by the way, handsome, have a cigar!"

"Madam, are you in quest of a kick in the pants?"

"Can I help it if I embarrassed the jury? I still say that's what I was doing on the night of June fourteenth"

"Now this one has a feature you'll like. If your kid monkeys with it while you're at the office, this car explodes and scares hell out of him"

"She says there's a gentleman on his way up—do we know a gentleman?"

*"—and I say help the British! If it wasn't for them, we'd be talking
some language we couldn't understand"*

"The people I belong to just <u>have</u> to be different"

"Ah me! So little time—so much to do"

"Will you stop running our daughter's life?"

"Take your dirty hand off my knee. No, not you. YOU!"

"Hello, darling, guess who!"

"I'd like something sensible for an elderly gentleman to drink champagne out of"

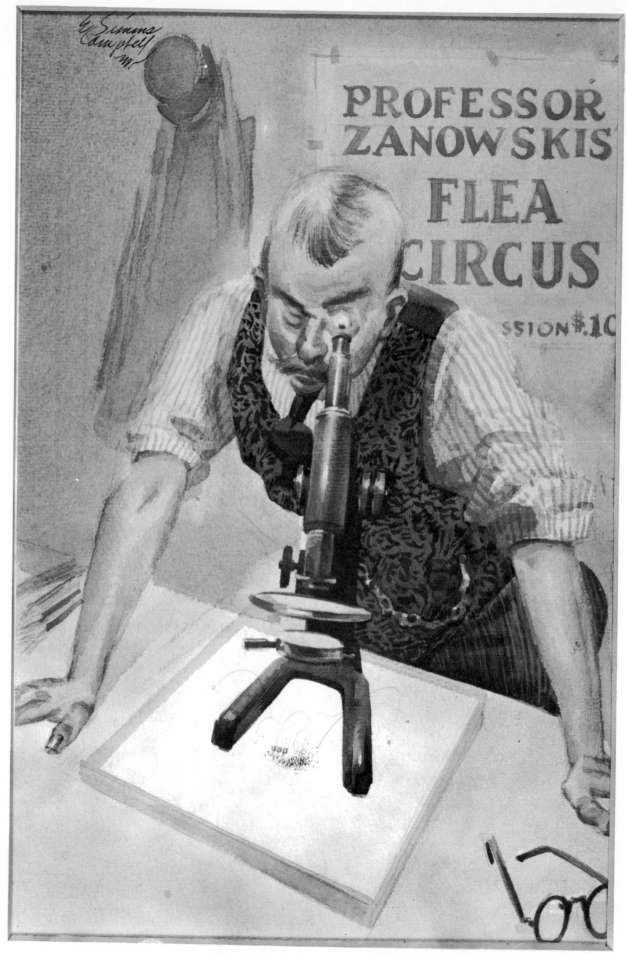

"Well, I'll be damned — picketing!"

"Oh for a girl, dear stars, even a cock-eyed girl!"

"If you hafta open the shutters lady, please,
for Lord's sake, put on a bathing suit!"

"Now which club do I use for a hole in one?"

"They told me to wait around for an answer"

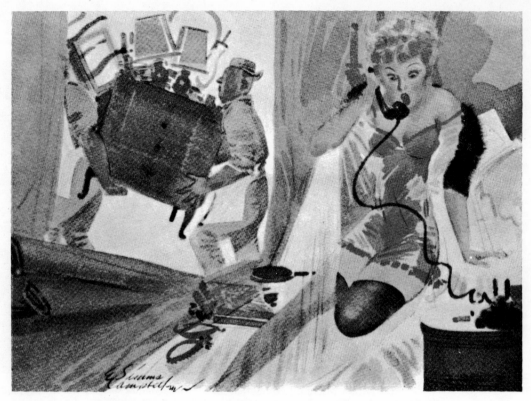

"Conference or no conference—you tell him it's 'Baby'
and it's mighty damn important!"

"I found two cosigners, so I won't need a loan after all!"

"There's some mix-up in the electric-blanket and
the automatic-toaster departments—people
are being popped out of bed!"

"*Who tore out the society page!*"

"All right, then—let's make it two out of three"

"Listen, dope! The way the mint makes 'em is good enough!
We don't want any improvements!"

"Very good, sir — as long as it's not a musical instrument"

"I used to know her — four checkbooks ago"

"No! Mother is not going swimming!"

"Now don't __you__ tell me to keep my head down!"

"Now __you__ guess who!"

"So then I says, 'Just because you own this business
is no sign you know how to run it!'"

"What's more, Mr. Simpson, I _demand_ a raise..."

"I wish you'd speak plainer, Mr. Frazer—
I can't read my notes!"

"The yacht he gave me leaked, the hair all came out of the sables, and now he gives me a diamond with a curse on it"

"Brothah, you ain't confessin', you's braggin'!"

"Fine friend you are—a little devaluation
of the pound and you leave"

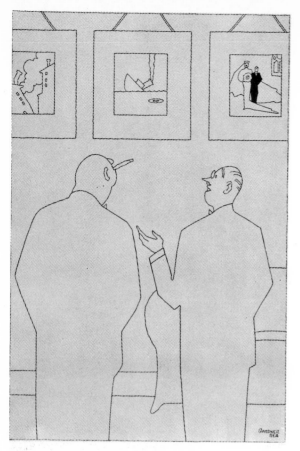

"The Chicago fire, the sinking of the Titanic,
and my marriage"

"First I was an apartment-house doorman.
Then I was a movie-theatre usher...
I guess I'm just a militarist at heart..."

"Keep an eye on this—I'm about to make
shoplifting history"

"Hello, Katherine Gibbs Secretarial School?—Help! Help!"

"We want something about 24″ x 37½″"

*"Next month, if I keep going at this rate, will make a year
that I've been faithful to Roger"*

"Couldn't you look a little more picturesque?"

"*You both know the rules—put the ring on her finger and go out fighting!*"

"I'm on guard duty, but why
in hell do you stay here?"

"You have nothing to fear but fear itself"

VOTE FOR
HONEST JOHN

LOW TAXES
BETTER GOVERNMENT

"...and they laugh at us for believing in Santa Claus!"

IF YOU MUST
SMOKE –
DO SO – THEN
LEAVE BY THE
EXIT·THAT WILL
SUDDENLY APPEAR
IN THE ROOF.

"For the others 'hors d'oeuvres,' but for you I got under the napkin, a hot pastrami sandwich"

"*My secretary couldn't come, so I brought my wife*"

"Here they come Reverend — like a bat out of Heaven"

"I'm sorry, Madam, but we have no shoes large on the inside
and small on the outside!"

"And remember—no Harvard boy ever
put anybody in the movies!"

"Social workers, Pet—Shall I give them
the ums-bay ush-ray?"

"How many times have I told you t'soive from d'left!"

"Jonesy certainly knows feminine psychology—his window is making a tremendous hit with the ladies"

"Roger Butterwing! Professor Smedley sent us out here to study botany!"

"White man, he say, 'What's Christmas without a tree?'"

"Taxi fare? Why, that's train fare!"

"Then you cross left and extend your right hand—
this, Miss La Burk, is your right hand"

"But I haven't any symptoms yet, Doctor—
you see, I only just heard about you"

"I think you should buy one for your wife—it's not
a very good reflection on me the way she goes around"

"Phil, you left your shaving brush out again"

"I got the idea from an airline company"

"Oh, John!...this is the boy next door
the neighbors wanted us to look after!"

"Oh yes, Darling—er—the plumber is here"

"She's got no visible means of support, Sarge!"

"Yes, indeed, dear — it is a surprise!"

"Why don't you move over here, Mr. Lowery, where you'll be closer to everything"

"Gee, Mr. Hodges—what odd territories
you give my husband"

"Of course I've seen his etchings but
what the hell are aquatints?"

"I think you'd better go home now,
Mr. Norton—it's Sunday"

"—make me a good girl and make Mr. Bixby's wife
give him a divorce"

"Did you have a tough day at the office, dear?"

"Did you have a tough night at home, dear?"

*"Don't you think it's kinda foolish t' spend a quarter for a diamond ring
ef we gonna keep our engagement a secret?"*

"May we have your opinion on this, Mr. Criddy?"

*"Could I change the last line of greeting number fifteen
to a request for ten bucks?"*

"You can stay if you want to, but I'm going home!"

"Not now! Mama is busy"

"Then the second movement goes like this"

"Damn Paw—stealin' my pants—I was figurin' on goin' to school today, too"

"*Now that was what I call a skirt sale*"

"*O.K. Rembrandt—where the hell's our planes!*"

"Lady, will you please take off your hat?"

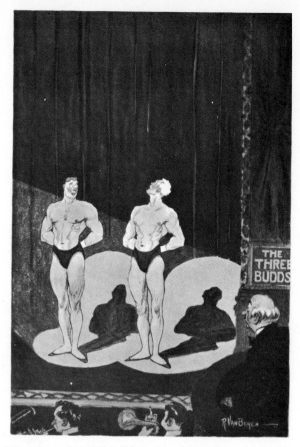

"You threw her. Why didn't you watch where she went?"

"Would you mind sharing your table with the dancer when she's through?"

"Goodness! You don't have to get nasty!"

"That's the sort of thing we're trying to discourage"

"*Beg pardon Mrs. Bixbee — I thought it was <u>Mr.</u> Bixbee*"

"We gotta let ya go, Steve, yuh just ain't got no showmanship!"

"Madame, it's this sort of thing that makes me inefficient!"

"Did Lincoln part his hair in the middle or on the side?"

"I'll teach you to bring dice to choir practice—
my point's nine!"

"It was his fault, dear—let him come to you!"

"Good Lord! This is the one I shot—
you're cooking the decoy!!"

"I was just tryin' to figure out what there is about you that Pop thinks is so hot"

"Ohh no—give me the worm _first_"

"I'd like to place a bet on the horse that's going to win"

"Don't lie to me—what's that I smell on your breath?"

"Who is that pillow?"

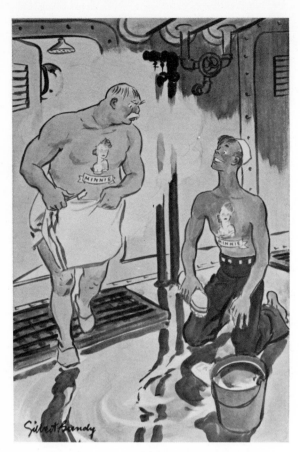

Well! Sort of a coincidence, eh Admiral?"

(Forty words deleted here)

"One short cheer—he only broke his collar bone"

*"I gues we all enjoy a news story
with a biological angle, don't we?"*

"No, no, Miss Balcom — this model buttons up the back!"

"—and that goes for you too, Smith!"

"Well if you really are the installment collector, there's someone in here swindling my roommate"

"But Mr. Scarponi...!"

"Let's stick around—this ought to be good!"

*"I'd rather not tell about the loaded dice episode—
I recognize a few o' the guys I played with"*

"Ahem—we came to rob the house—at first"

"That's quite all right. Pardon my glove, too"

*"Attempted arson, attempted robbery,
attempted murder—gave up trying!"*

"You're asking for a raise at a rather bad time, Wilkingson—my wife has her eye on a robin's-egg blue Cadillac convertible"

"*¿Tiene Nembutal?*"

"*Hot damn! Only ten minutes more and it's
time for siesta*"

"Now I mail one copy to Santa Claus and duplicates to Mr. Gelespie, Mr. Tyson, Mr. Salisbury and Major Holbrook just to make sure"

"Dolores! I resent tradesmen!"

"Of course you can take me home—where do you live?"

"Maybe it was something you ate, dear"

"I'll give them 'til nine-thirty—if they aren't here then, I break training!"

"Pa musta got the damn gears in backwards— she goes mighty good though, don't she?"

"But what __are__ birds, bees and flowers?"

"Don't forget—tonight we make a break for it"

"—and tell 'em this last brandy was lousy"

"It looks like the whole damn convention is going to be held in this room"

"I want something to go with a blonde"

"Were you expecting the sheriff, sir?"

"No! No! Miss Welton!—For the last time,
it's Western Sporting Goods House!"

"Miss Stern, this is a liberal magazine! Why should
we give a damn what our readers think?"

"You may not realize it, Miss Goodrich, but you've broken the hearts
of the entire fourth grade!"

"Goodness, I haven't told my husband yet—how did you know?"

"Dear will you give this man some money? He held me up but I explained about your handling the money"

"I'm going to study and improve myself and when you're still a common thief I'll be an embezzler"

"But Miss Wiggins, just how did you think little girls got to be movie stars?"

"See here, Radcliffe — that girl's mind isn't on her work!"

"That's just what I'm afraid of—that you <u>are</u> old enough"

"Marie, your boy friend has been here five months— is he going to spend the night?"

"So that's the way you take care of things while I'm away!"

"Well, <u>one</u> thing—she's a damn good secretary"

"He was just about the most unforgettable character
I've ever met!"

"I guess I better send out after a bone to keep Fifi quiet"

"I want to get a screen test—what do I do—
just walk right in?"

"*I really think it's just a slang expression. I've never had ants in mine*"

"You aren't the Mr. Penny I came here with!"

"Naw, that's not his wife, that's real ermine"

"The police put my husband in a padded cell—he refused to come home with me so they concluded he was crazy"

"He's outlasted three husbands!"

"Okay! Okay! So it'll stop on a dime!"

"Do I have to pay any duty on her? I got her in France!"

"You should have seen it before I shrunk it"

"In this day of push-button machines, man has forgotten
the basic art of doing for himself"

*"I have some beautiful etchings—wait right here
and I'll bring them down"*

"What! Me ride with you and your—your paramour!"

"Oh, you're different"

"Missus Reed-Smith-Woffington residence—no, Missus ain't in, Mista Woffington, she's out with Mista Reed"

"Looks like we're goin' to have corn pone tonight—Gran'maw is looking up the recipe ag'in"

"Take off yer hat!"

"I understand the bunch on the next car is already plotting a <u>counter</u> revolution"

"My husband, poor dear—he's working late again"

"You realize, of course, that this tells us
absolutely nothing"

"Whom do you call in a case like this?"

"When it boils right down, I had more actual cash
when I was in your notions department, Mr. Simons"

*"Of course I want you to answer the phone!—
What do you think I hired you for?"*

*"I **can't** throw him out—he's the sponsor of the program"*

*"Now that's a new line—who ever heard
of running out of snow"*

*"Oh yes, doctor—the patient in 42 has no pulse, no
temperature and no heartbeat. That's all"*

"*Say the words that will make me the happiest man in the world—say you'll be mine, Mr. Swejckowski, for $62.50 plus overtime*"

"Here comes Julius now"

"When you call her a tramp, you don't have to convince _me_—
it's the audience out there!"

"We'll wait five minutes more—then if we don't get a date we'll open the sardines and eat"

"Honor'ble Chairman, Mister President, and members o' de board—dis is a stick-up!"

"*Quick, slip that dress off! Here comes a couple of photographers from the National Geographic*"

"*It's a hot day, Ed, and you had too many beers maybe*"

"*Oh-h-h—let it ring!*"

"*You'd think the damn fools never saw baskets before*"

"Do you really like 'em?—I think they're terrible of me"

"Two more quarts and two more hostesses"

"Well do something—don't just stand there!"

"WHAT—more bread?—an' not a drop
of whisky in th' house!"

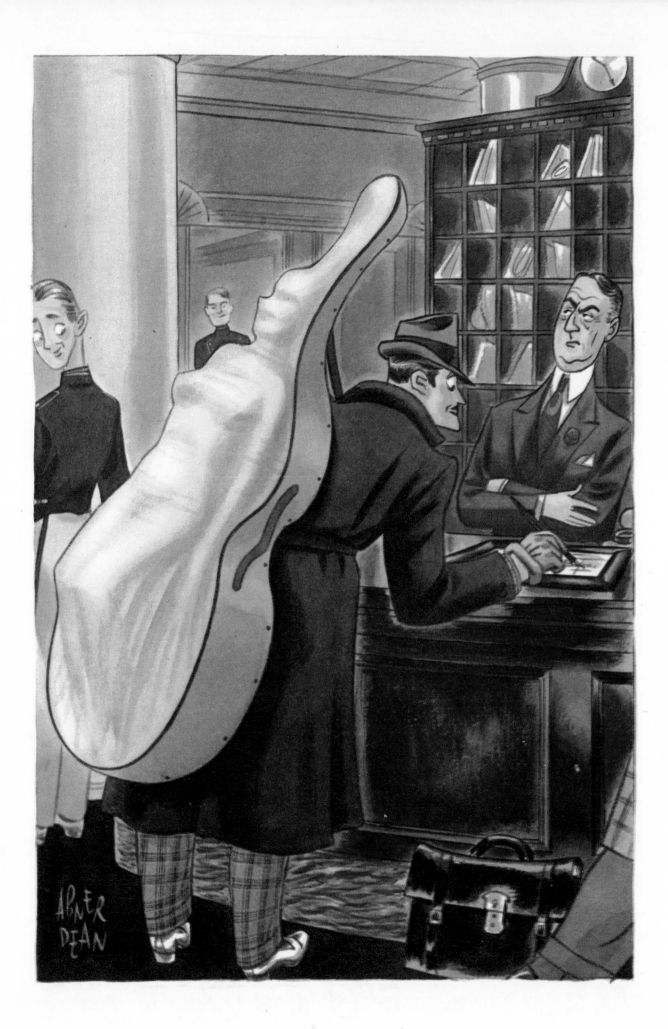

"Pardon sir, did you promise matrimony
to a Miss Toots O'Leary?"

"Good Lord, Ferguson—you oughta see
what you got them puppets doing!"

"Trouble is, I'm the type that mother
won't let me associate with"

"Listen, Mac—go find your own island!"

"I know it's silly—but I could have sworn
I heard a cow just then!"

"When I joined, I thought it was the American Legion"

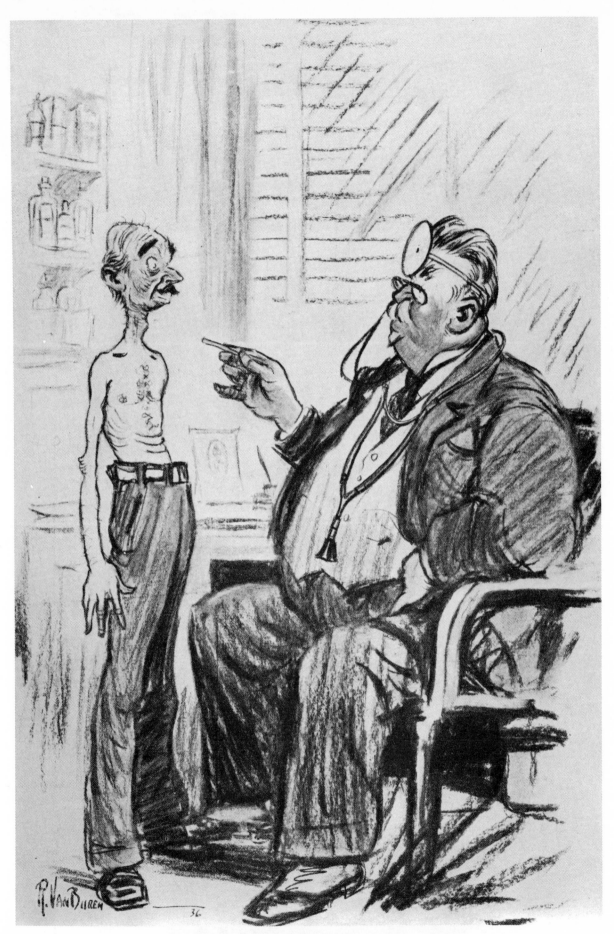

"Better lay off the health foods for awhile"

"*You're a poet! Now what the hell kind of racket is that?*"

"Well, what do you say, Jack — shall we call it a day?"

"My house—my pajamas"

"Cigarette? Or did I prescribe no smoking for you?"

*"Frankly, Miss Jennings, when I gave you this apartment,
I expected a little more for Christmas"*

"Do you mind if I add 'You Rat!' to Christmas Greeting number thirty-two?"

"Santa Claus my foot, you get the hell out of here"

"Well, Prince, since you've made the little girl a Princess, that sort of makes me some sort of something, eh?"

"Two months he's been like that—somebody he never heard of sent him a Xmas card"

"What a perfectly ridiculous idea, darling—of course you're the only one I ever loved!"

"Eight bells and all's well, Madam"

"Mr. Rogin brought orchids, Mr. Stren brought gardenias and your husband brought Junior"

"That reminds me—I forgot about that form letter that was to go out today"

"What! You aren't the casting director?"

"At about this time he was struggling to perfect a new technique"

"They opened the door and let in another bull while he was bowing to the crowd"

"Oh, boy—what wouldn't I give to see her in an evening gown!"

"*But you couldn't be Mrs. Parsons—she just checked in here with Mr. Parsons*"

*"Paw sez thars a rumor goin' 'round
Hoover ain't president no more"*

"One billion dollars on the red"

"Shall we dance? Oh how silly…we are dancing, aren't we?"

*"She's Warner Bros.' new star—she's vacationing here
to escape publicity"*

"I like you older men — young men are so broke"

"Stand by the window a minute, Honey—
I want to burn up that bachelor"

"Mr. Schnerr! Aren't you putting the cart
before the horse?"

"Sorry, Herman, but I'll have to let you go"

"Would you say 'I hereby resign'—or make it
more informal, like 'I quit'?"

"Would you care to take it inside and see how it looks under artificial light?"

"You mean you won't marry me at all—not even for a little while?"

"Shore—Ah knows tomorrow's only Thanksgiving—but who knows, we might oversleep"

"Yeah, your honor—I been up for bigamy, arson, forgery, assault 'n' batt'ry and burglary—but heck—nobody's perfect!"

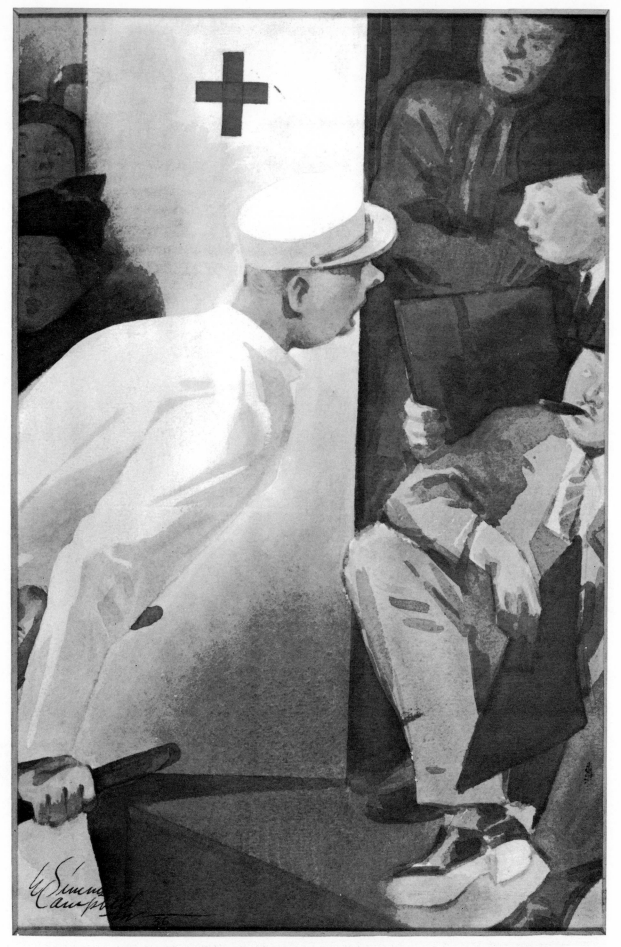

"One of you lawyers will have to get out and make room for the patient"

"What a moon—just imagine the power of <u>that</u> advertising space!"

"You can be sure of one thing—if there are fantastic weapons, they'll be heavy"

"Are you <u>sure</u> you take this—to be your lawful, wedded husband?"

"Grandpa—are you going to leave your money to Papa or outlive us all just for spite, like Mama says?"

"Come now—just be natural. You've taken a bath before, haven't you?"

"An apéritif"

"All right, Lover Boy, watch it!"

"He's paying me fifty thousand dollars to get back his letters but I'm retaining the movie rights"

"Ladies, would you like to earn $90 to $100 a week?
The Bloopo Manufacturing Company has immediate
openings for 300 ladies. No experience necessary.
Learn the interesting, new trade of…"

"This is where you two came in"

"Amen!"

"Darling, your eyes are like limpid pools"

"Oh well—I practically got them the same way"

"Do you have French Frys?"

"Would you mind getting the hell outa the way?"

"*It's the only way we can get him to inhale the ether*"

"Remember now—before the guests it's 'Join me in a game of billiards' and not 'How about shootin' some pool'!"

"For devotion beyond the line of duty"

"Young man—if you work any more around here after hours—you're fired!"

"Use your imagination!"

"What makes you so vulnerable?"

"And there's a mortgage on the old homestead — but I don't know why I'm telling you all this, Mr. Calvert?"

"I'd ruther starve!"

"Birth control? — Oh, dat's all right for you, Missy Jones. But ah'm married"

"Son, that's what I call art with a capital A"

"Well, it's up to you lady, whether we go up or not!"

"Sure they're potent, and they're very strong, too"

"Would you mind putting on the lights a minute, dear?
I can't find the knife and fork"

"How does it feel, son, to be taking an active part in business now?"

"He's sort of continental — kisses your hand,
orders in French, and gives you the check..."

"Isn't that gorgeous, Myrt? It's got
four hundred and six genuine crystals"

"But — but it's only noon!"

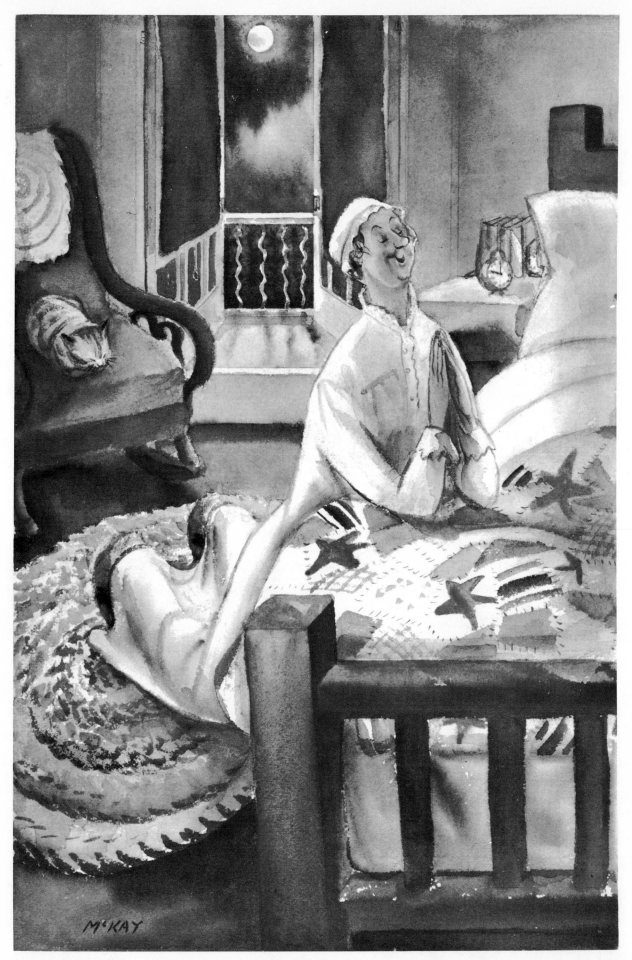

"Ah! Men!"

"I see you've forgotten the glasses again"

"Of course I love you—but I'd be a lot happier
if I could go out with the boys once in awhile"

"Father's Day greetings, sir—collect!"

"It helped pay for their honeymoon"

"I'm in a devilish jam—they've gone and drafted my tailor!"

"One Mickey Finn, please — my husband suggested it!"

"W-a-all Street Final!"

*"Everybody else seems to be able to get
a cost-of-living increase"*

"Agnes! We're in style again!"

"It *is* a violin!"

"All right, Egbert—let him have it!"

"Now, aren't you ashamed of yourself?"

"The Union says we've got to use three men"

"Dames is poison"

"The <u>hands</u> don't express anything!"

*"—and let me, my darling, rest—
my weary head upon your breast"*

"But that's impossible, Doctor. I'm not even married!"

"What do you mean <u>look</u> scared — I am scared!"

*"We would like to know, my companions and I,
if this train is air-conditioned"*

"Doesn't this remind you of some place you've been before?"

"Oh H-a-a-r-r-r-vey—I've changed my mind—"

"Dhawalagiri—it's about men and a mountain!"

"I don't know how long we've been here, Captain—we've had no way of keeping track of the years"

"Could I see your seat stubs, please?"

"My wife—my friend—my vintage port!"

"Ah ah—I'm gonna tell the maid you're kissing mamma!"

'But why on earth should our housemaid go to your office and shoot your secretary?''

"Just ta-ra, ta-ra, ta-ra and not so much wah-wah!"

*"I've been here three weeks and seen everything
but New York"*

"Doll for Mr. Winters!"

"Madam ain't at home—by Gawd!"

"That's my husband over there—the medium-well"

"By Gad, Wilkens! There's a real old-fashioned girl!"

"There are two ways of becoming a star, Miss Tulare—one is by industry, concentration and perseverance—the other I think might interest you"

"Let me off quick, there's no one driving!"

"I wish my husband could see how suave you are"

"I wonder when he's gonna start paintin' her?"

"Now each pin indicates the position of a salesman
visiting a client, except these over here—
that's a blonde in Kansas City"

"So that made it __our__ ball on Army's five yard line"

"Oh, you would — would you!

"Sometimes I think our divorce was a mistake"

"Hello, Peter. You can go to hell now"

"Would you ask that gentleman at the next table
if he would like to join us?"

"*I know your wages are small, Marie — but after all, you're learning*"

"Gosh, Honey, the way we fight anyone would think we were married"

"That's the trouble...My own mother didn't know me nobody does"

"After a year as his secretary, he pulls this typewriting and shorthand stuff on me"

"I make a motion we do all this again sometime"

"Did the whale swallow Jonah—will Jonah escape? What will happen? Don't miss next Sunday's thrilling episode"

"Professor Chadwick, I understand you spoke harshly to our triple threat man!"

"I think it's wonderful you're so democratic and everything, Reverend!"

"What's this!!—a letter?"

"Wonder if Maw's had her baby yet
—I'm gettin' mighty hongry"

"Maybe if _I_ went away for awhile—?"

"Yoo hoo—Darling and Mr. Baxter—I've found the ball!"

"Chief? This is O'Rourke—wanna hear something funny?"

"Well, I see they're reviving that Santa myth again"

"I hate to break up his rest, but I was supposed to get off three stations back"

"It isn't bad enough that we have guests — now our guests are having guests!"

"I'm sorry—but one of you dames will have
to go chase herself!"

"—and remember, none of that hi do ho stuff!"

"My word, isn't that Twillingsby?"

"I've had three colonels and a general shot from under me!"

"There's a lady to see you, Mr. Larkin. Says you had a ten o'clock appointment with her"

"Why are we leaving? I just happened to remember— that's our house"

"Mingle, dear! Circulate!"

"While you were out, your Mr. Drake called— let's just call him our Mr. Drake from now on"

"Well, this is the part where I came in—it was nice knowing you!"

"I know the street is Broadway, dagnab it!! What I want to know is the name of the town!"

"Pardon me, does any of you happen to be my wife?"

"I have not been indiscreet every time your back is turned!"

"Well, if we have to have $12,000,000, I suggest
we borrow it from the union"

"You've convinced me, Miss Clark. Will you come in now
and take a letter?"

"M-m-m—so it isn't daughter's money he's after at all"

"Do you suppose it would do any good to speak to her union again?"

"Come! Come!—You must regard her simply as a machine that must be repaired"

"You're fired! Both of you!"

"*I want to report this phone out of order — I haven't had a call all evening*"

"It's from the World's Fair Committee—they're not interested in our idea for a concession!"

"_Now_ let's hear you sing"

"Mr. Woodring?...Mr. Woodring, to settle a bet,
what the hell came off in your office today?"

"Wouldn't it be more sensible, dear,
to just spend our money foolishly?"

"But mama, he's busy with a buyer"

"You're right, Agnes — Faust's trousers are slipping"

"*My youngest daughter, Jane—I was afraid she was going to be a wallflower but she was named correspondent in a divorce case yesterday!*"

"Good heavens! Clothes certainly do make the man!"

"*That* ain't no directors' meeting!"

"I always know when I've had enough to drink—
I become unconscious!"

"Get me that book on appendicitis"

"I'se never been X-rayed, but I'se been ultra-violated!"

"He says he was watching his hat and someone stole his wife"

"Sometimes I think I'll have one just for the hell of it"

"For the last time Mr. Corbett—my name is Marie, not Fanny!"

"In case she sends me out looking for you later, sir,
where shouldn't I go?"

"Always wait for the red light—__then__ if you get hit you can sue"

"Who's that!—Joe?—Alec?—Terry?"

"Well, well—you people still using the old telephone, I see!"

"The zipper came with the dress, but the padlock is my own idea"

"Sweetheart, I've walked him 'round the block three times,
but he doesn't seem to realize—"

"Meecham loves to sit and dream before the fire for hours"

"Paging Mr. Morris Goldwyn—Mr. Morris Goldwyn, Exclusive
Misses' Dresses, 141 Broadway—paging Mr. Morris—"

"—Maybe you'd better give them your consent after all, dear"

"I don't see any parade"

"I just thought I'd drop back to see if you had any dictation"

"Your honeymoon will take you through much new territory
and I want you to keep a sharp lookout
for possible industrial sites"

"I'd like to see how you'd handle today's tax setup with all that keen, fearless wisdom of yours"

"Is it anyone we know?"

"Mama, Wilfred wrote a bad word!"

"Aw, come on in, baby—the wife's still down south"

"Our first foul ball, Emily"

"*How do you suppose they hang on upside down?*"

"She say you know what you can do with
yo' weddin' invitation, Mistuh Tommy"

"All right, so I'm dumb, so what would you do
with a cultured woman?"

"She never goes anywhere without a chaperone"

"*I don't like it!*"

"I don't care if you can afford it, Mr. Thurman—we discourage bringing secretaries to class to take notes!"

"But dear—don't you find it hard to work
with that orchestra in your office!"

"Gosh, lady, but you startled me—for a moment
I thought you were Marlene Dietrich"

"I can't understand it—they stop and look,
but they don't go in"

"Say, whose trial is this anyway?"

"Sometimes I almost wish I'd rescued that blonde
instead of the Harvard Classics!"

"Hello Ma! Hello Pa! It was a great fight...
I'll be home soon!"

"We taught him to talk—but the reading was his own idea!"

"Madam is taking a bawth—but I'll tell her you phoned"

"The hell with him — no judge would ever believe this old heap could do over fifteen miles per hour!"

"I was starving to death with a monkey"

"Just sprinkle this on, lady—and then jump away quick!"

"Dot's de American frum opstairs"

"Elmer, sometimes I wonder what the hell I ever saw in you!"

"Oh — er — hello, Harkins — I thought I was the only one home"

"Thanks for the hospitality, Mrs. Prentice, but what's this about you shooting your husband?"

"Ah, Marie! It's good to be in love"

"I don't want to seem over zealous, mam, but I think it's about time you bought a brush."

"Hell no—it's just sheer whimsey"

"Close your eyes, Doctor, I'm coming out"

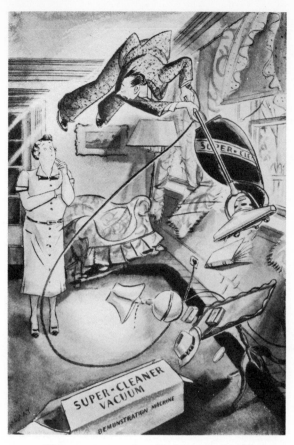

"It's not supposed to do this, of course!"

"You men make me sick — standing around talking while the party goes stale"

"Somebody in this car has cold hands!"

"Why, Mr. Mandel, you've forgotten your violin tonight"

"*Never mind my orange sherbet, Lady Clavering—I'll go fetch another!*"

"It's Pop! And he's holding up a man on each arm again!"

"—but can't _I_ have something besides my picture on the sardine can?"

"Sorry—you'll have to put a tie on!"

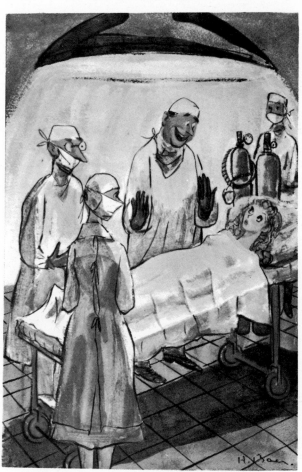

"Will your scar show? That's up to you, beautiful"

"You're just wasting your time—I'm not going to shut the water off till you leave the room!"

"Just brushing up, sir...I get out tomorrow"

"Would your wife care if I used a guest towel, Mr. Cutney?"

"Why, Mr. DeMunson! You're not painting me at all!"

"See—to get rid of the surplus, we merely add a bunch of grapes and transfer them to the millinery department"

"I met the nicest man on my honeymoon!"

"Damn! Can't you even <u>cook</u>?"

"What fire?"

"I don't care if you <u>did</u> hear me call daddy that.
Don't use <u>those</u> words again!"

"Please don't feel it necessary to make conversation"

"*Yes he's awfully nice — youngest father I've ever had*"

"*I'm sorry, Mrs. Conway, but this is a matter <u>solely</u> between your son, my daughter, the Ajax Hotel and Reverend Ferguson*"

"Mother always make me write it five hundred times before I go out with Mr. Parker"

"You may go in now"

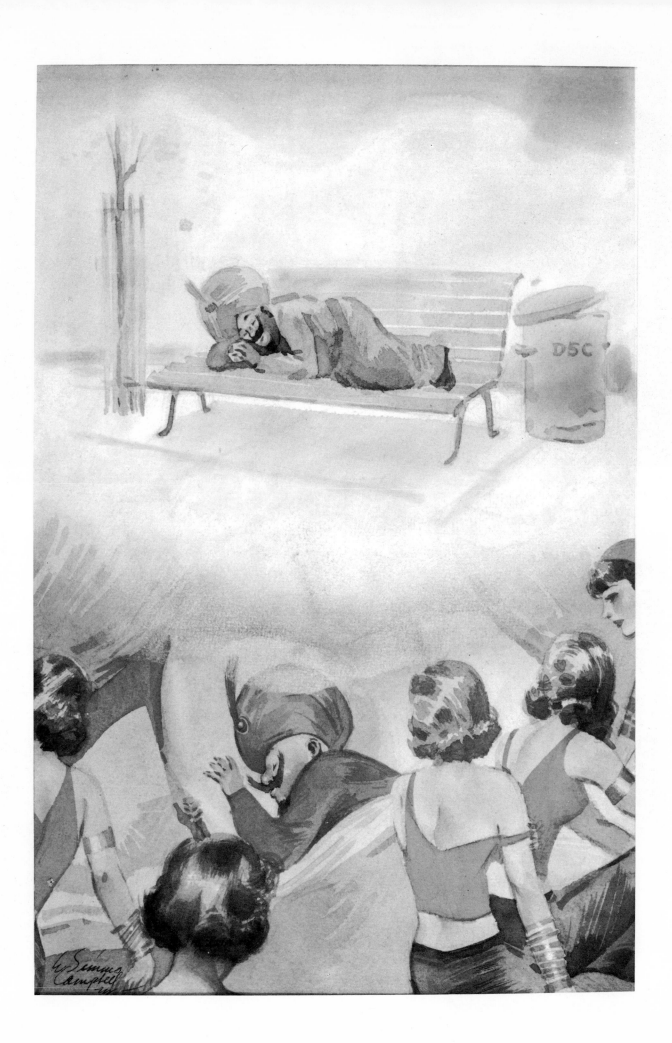

"I'm sorry but I never accept gifts from strange men—
why don't you come up and get acquainted?"

"Do you folks—er—mind if I tell a clean one?"

"Righto"

"A buck an' a half I give him fer liquor an' he comes back
with a French berry hat!"

"It's Marcusson—stealing Goldwater's exclusive styles that we stole from Himmelman!"

"My first case—my law school is suing me for tuition"

"Good heavens dear, don't turn on the light— Mr. Arturo is telling me a ghost story"

"Oh!—So now you're in a hurry!"

"I understand you discovered Streptomycin — who lost it?"

"Did I hear someone knocking?"

"She's marvelous with the children, too"

"Shouldn't one of us write a 'thank you' note
to the First National?"

"Will you bring home an erector set for Junior, dear — I think he's getting too old to play with blocks"

"Merry Christmas, mamma and daddy"

"Darling, could you let me take that marked deck? I want to show Mrs. Wilson the trick you taught me"

"I'm getting fed up—it's just one damn thing
after another ever since I've had it"

"You can lead a horse to water, Mr. Gerhart—"

"Hey driver! Is there a Justice of the Peace between here
and the hospital? We forgot something"

"Good afternoon, ladies and gentlemen"

"Late again!"

"To hell with the instruments—when my corn twitches there's a storm abrewin'"

ARTISTS REPRESENTED IN THIS ALBUM

HOWARD BAER'S cartoons, illustrations and paintings have been a regular feature in Esquire since the first issue. His paintings have been exhibited in one-man shows here and in Paris, and are in the permanent collections of the Metropolitan Museum, the Butler Art Institute and the Pentagon War Archives.

RAEBURN VAN BUREN began as a sketch artist on the Kansas City Star, studied at New York's Art Students League, and freelanced as illustrator and cartoonist from 1913 until his "Abbie An' Slats" comic strip laid full claim to his time. It now appears in about 300 papers around the world and is over 20 years old.

E. SIMMS CAMPBELL has been Esquire's most prolific creator of cartoons, and has never missed an issue. He attended the University of Chicago and Chicago Art Institute, holds honorary degrees from two other universities, is a charter member of the National Cartoonists Society, has illustrated a dozen books and written numerous articles on jazz.

DOROTHY McKAY'S cartoons, covers and illustrations appeared regularly in the old Life, College Humor, New Yorker, Ballyhoo and Forum until, she says, "Esquire began to corral my time — from the second issue on." She grew up in San Francisco, where she studied at the California School of Fine Arts until she moved to New York.

SYD HOFF'S drawings have appeared in Esquire since the third issue, February 1934. He was born in New York, attended the National Academy of Design, studying fine art. "Since magazines began buying my first cartoons," he says, "I stuck with it." He lives in Miami Beach, Florida.

PAUL WEBB has been famous for his Mountain Boys cartoons since they first appeared in Esquire's first year. Previously, he studied at Philadelphia's School of Industrial Arts and Academy of Fine Arts, won two traveling scholarships to Europe, sold cartoons to the old Life, Judge, College Humor, Colliers and New Yorker. He lives in Connecticut.

ELDON DEDINI attended the Chouinard Art Institute in Los Angeles and worked for Universal and Disney studios before beginning his regular contributions to Esquire in 1945. He lives in Monterey, California where, he says, "with a group of 'paisanos' we meet in Doc's old place on Cannery Row, studying wines, jazz and philosophy."

GARRETT PRICE left the wilds of Wyoming at nineteen to study at Chicago's Art Institute. He worked as artist and layout man on the Chicago Tribune and as editorial cartoonist for the Great Lakes Bulletin until 1925, when he started free-lancing in New York. He now divides his time between Westport and Mason's Island, Connecticut.

PLUS:

CONSTANTIN ALAJALOV
C. W. ANDERSON
TONY BARLOW
FRANK BEAVEN
SHEILAH BECKETT
HENRY BOLTINOFF
BO BROWN
GILBERT BUNDY
IRWIN CAPLAN
CHARLES H. CARTWRIGHT
BILL CHARMATZ
ROLAND COE
JON CORNIN
R. CZERMANSKI
GREGORY D'ALESSIO
RODNEY deSARRO
ABNER DEAN
ROBERT C. DELL

JEAN DUGO
CAL DUNN
JARO FABRY
ANDRE FRANÇOIS
LEO GAREL
ARTHUR GETZ
DENVER GILLEN
ALEXANDRE STEEL GRAHAM
GERD GRIMM
JOHN GROTH
NED HILTON
ROBERT HOLLEY
OSCAR HOWARD
ED HUNTER
JAY IRVING
LOUIS JAMME
REAMER KELLER
LAWRENCE LARIAR
ROBERT J. LEE
ARTHUR FRANK LEMON
HERBERT LEUPIN

GEORGE LICHTY
MIKE LUDLOW
FRED LUNDY
TY MAHON
FRANKO MARAZ
JERRY MARCUS
BABETTE NEWBURGER
BILL O'MALLEY
WILLIAM PACHNER
BOB PAPLOW
GEORGE PETTY
IRVING PHILLIPS
JOHN PIEROTTI
GARDNER REA
JULIETTE KIDA RENAULT
KEN RICHARDS
MISCHA RICHTER
WILLIAM RIENECKE
IRVING ROIR
CARL ROSE
DICK ROSE

A. ROSS
BEN ROTH
ADOLPH SCHUS
GEORGE SHELLHASE
BARBARA SHERMUND
EVERETT SHINN
ARNOLD SPILKA
WALTER F. SPRINK
STANLEY STAMATY
WILLIAM STEIG
SUSI STEINITZ
RICHARD TAYLOR
BARNEY TOBEY
GOBI UPPENBERG
JEAN VAN SAUN
WILLIAM VON RIEGEN
CHARLES WEINERT
LEO WEISZ
FRITZ WILKINSON
GEORGE WOLFE
ALEX YOUNG